CAVALCADE OF POEMS

CAVALCADE OF POEMS

GEORGE BENNETT and PAUL MOLLOY

The Phillips Exeter Academy

cover photo by Alan Rabold

Published by Scholastic Book Services, a division of
Scholastic Magazines, Inc.

For reprint permission grateful acknowledgement is made to:

George Allen & Unwin Ltd. for "The Hammers" from THE LAST BLACKBIRD by R. Hodgson.

John Baker, Publishers, Ltd. for "A Runnable Stag" by John Davidson.

The Belknap Press of Harvard University Press for "The Snow" and "A Narrow Fellow in the Grass" from THE POEMS OF EMILY DICKINSON, edited by Thomas H. Johnson, copyright 1951, 1955 by The President and Fellows of Harvard College; and to Little, Brown and Co., publishers of THE COMPLETE POEMS OF EMILY DICKINSON.

Bowes & Bowes Publishers Ltd. for "The Country Bedroom" by Frances Cornford.

Brandt & Brandt for "Nancy Hanks" by Rosemary Carr Benét from A BOOK OF AMERICANS by Rosemary and Stephen Vincent Benét, published by Holt, Rinehart and Winston, Inc. Copyright 1933 by Rosemary and Stephen Vincent Benét, copyright renewed 1961 by Rosemary Carr Benét.

J. M. Dent & Sons Ltd. and the Literary Executors of the Dylan Thomas Estate for Canadian rights to "Hunchback in the Park" from THE COLLECTED POEMS OF DYLAN THOMAS.

Doubleday & Co., Inc. for "The Snake" by Kyoshi, "Barley Field" by Sora, "Barley Field" by Joso from AN INTRODUCTION TO HAIKU by Harold G. Henderson, copyright © 1958 by Harold G. Henderson; for "The Heron," copyright 1937 by Theodore Roethke from WORDS FOR THE WIND by Theodore Roethke.

Paul Eldridge for "The Moth and the Lamp" by Paul Eldridge (originally titled "Quam Tsi Tung").

Norma Millay Ellis for "The Buck in the Snow" from COLLECTED POEMS by Edna St. Vincent Millay, published by Harper & Row, Publishers, copyright 1928 by Edna St. Vincent Millay, renewed 1955 by Norma Millay Ellis.

Lois E. Engleman for "In a Vacant Lot" from AUTUMN OFFERINGS by Anna U. Engleman.

Faber & Faber Ltd. for Canadian rights to "My Parents Kept Me From Children Who Were Rough" from COLLECTED POEMS BY STEPHEN SPENDER.

Charlie May Fletcher for "The Skaters" by John Gould Fletcher.

Robert Francis for "That Dark Other Mountain," copyright 1943, 1944 by Robert Francis from THE SOUND I LISTENED FOR by Robert Francis, published by The Macmillan Company.

Samuel French, Inc. for "Deer" from POEMS 1908-1919, copyright 1919 by John Drinkwater, published by Houghton Mifflin Co.

Mrs. Norene Carr Grace, Executrix, for "Skaters" by Frances Frost.

Harcourt, Brace & World, Inc. for: "Above the Dock" from SPECULATIONS by T. E. Hulme; for "Boy at the Window," Copr. © 1952 The New Yorker Magazine, Inc. from THINGS OF THIS WORLD by Richard Wilbur; for "Chanson Innocent" from POEMS 1923-1954 by E. E. Cummings, copyright 1923, 1951 by E. E. Cummings.

Harper and Row, Publishers for "Sea Gulls" from STUDIES IN POETRY by Neal Doubleday, copyright 1949 by Harper & Brothers.

Rupert Hart-Davis Ltd. for "The Chalk Cliff" by Andrew Young.

Holt, Rinehart and Winston, Inc. for: "Blue-Butterfly Day," "Dust of Snow," "The Line-Gang" and "The Runaway" from COMPLETE POEMS OF ROBERT FROST, Copyright 1916, 1921, 1923 by Holt, Rinehart and Winston, Inc., Copyright renewed 1944, 1951 by Robert Frost; for "Questioning Faces" from IN THE CLEARING by Robert Frost, copyright © 1962 by Robert Frost; for "Under a Telephone Pole" from CHICAGO POEMS by Carl Sandburg, Copyright 1916 by Holt, Rinehart and Winston, Inc., Copyright renewed 1944 by Carl Sandburg; for "Eight O'Clock" from COMPLETE POEMS by A. E. Housman, Copyright 1922 by Holt, Rinehart and Winston, Inc., Copyright renewed 1950 by Barclays Bank Ltd.; "Reveille" from "A Shropshire Lad"—Authorized Edition—from COMPLETE POEMS by A. E. Housman, Copyright © 1959 by Holt, Rinehart and Winston, Inc.

Edwin Honig for "Outer Drive" by Edwin Honig from *Saturday Review*, July 7, 1956.

Houghton Mifflin Co. for "The Fish" by Elizabeth Bishop.

Alfred A. Knopf, Inc. for "The Victim," "Memory," and 21 lines of "Pastoral" from COLLECTED POEMS, © 1961 by Robert Hillyer; "August" by Elinor Wylie, copyright 1921 by Alfred A. Knopf, Inc., renewed 1949 by William Rose Benét from COLLECTED POEMS by Elinor Wylie; "The Wayfarer" and "I Saw a Man" from THE COLLECTED POEMS OF STEPHEN CRANE, published 1930 by Alfred A. Knopf, Inc.

Melvin Walker La Follette for "The Ballad of Red Fox" by Melvin Walker La Follette, Copr. © 1952 The New Yorker Magazine, Inc.

The Macmillan Co. for "The Dark Hills" from COLLECTED POEMS by Edwin Arlington Robinson, copyright 1920 by Edwin Arlington Robinson, renewed 1948 by Ruth Nivison; for "Crystal Moment" from COLLECTED POEMS by Robert P. Tristram Coffin, copyright 1932 by The Macmillan Co., renewed 1960 by Margaret Halvosa; "Cargoes" from COLLECTED POEMS by John Masefield, copyright 1912 by The Macmillan Company, renewed 1940 by John Masefield; for "The MouseThat Gnawed the Oak Tree Down" and "The Broncho That Would Not Be Broken" from COLLECTED POEMS by Vachel Lindsay, copyright 1914, 1917 by The Macmillan Co., renewed 1943, 1945 by Elizabeth C. Lindsay; for "The Man He Killed" from COLLECTED POEMS by Thomas Hardy.

The Macmillan Company of Canada Ltd., the Trustees of the Hardy Estate, and Macmillan & Co. Ltd., London for Canadian rights to "The Man He Killed" from COLLECTED POEMS OF THOMAS HARDY.

John Murray (Publishers) Ltd. for "Seaside Golf" from COLLECTED POEMS by John Betjeman.

New Directions, Publishers for: "Brimming Water" by Tu Fu from ONE HUNDRED POEMS FROM THE CHINESE translated by Kenneth Rexroth, all rights reserved; for "The Red Wheelbarrow" from COLLECTED EARLIER POEMS OF WILLIAM CARLOS WILLIAMS, copyright 1938, 1951 by W. C. Williams; for "The Hunchback in the Park" from THE COLLECTED POEMS OF DYLAN THOMAS, copyright 1953 by Dylan Thomas, © 1957 by New Directions.

Oxford University Press for "The Fox" from THE BALLAD OF KON-TIKI by Ian Serraillier.

Random House, Inc. for "My Parents Kept Me From Children Who Were Rough" from POEMS BY STEPHEN SPENDER, copyright 1934 and renewed 1961 by Stephen Spender; for "Evening Ebb" from THURSO'S LANDING, DEAR JUDAS AND OTHER POEMS by Robinson Jeffers, copyright 1929 and renewed 1957 by Robinson Jeffers, and reprinted from THE SELECTED POETRY OF ROBINSON JEFFERS; for "Pelicans" reprinted from ROAN STALLION, TAMAR, AND OTHER POEMS, copyright 1925 and renewed 1953 by Robinson Jeffers.

The Ryerson Press, Toronto, for "The Forsaken" from THE SELECTED POEMS OF DUNCAN CAMPBELL SCOTT.

St. Martin's Press, Inc. for "Boats at Night" from POEMS 1912-32 by Edward Shanks, published by Macmillan & Co. Ltd., London.

Martin Secker & Warburg Ltd. for "The Old Ships" by James Elroy Flecker.

Karl Shapiro for "Manhole Covers" by Karl Shapiro.

Sheed and Ward for "Parachutist" from DISCOVERY AND OTHER POEMS by Samuel Hazo.

The Society of Authors, representatives of the Literary Trustees of Walter de la Mare, for "Silver," "An Epitaph," "The Moth," and "The Listeners" by Walter de la Mare; literary representatives of the Estate of the late A. E. Housman, and Messrs. Jonathan Cape Ltd. for Canadian rights to "Eight O'Clock" and "Reveille" from COLLECTED POEMS by A. E. Housman.

Helen Thomas for "Tall Nettles" from COLLECTED POEMS by Edward Thomas.

The Viking Press for "Memory of Lake Superior" from THE FLOWERING STONE by George Dillon, copyright 1931, 1959 by George Dillon; for "Shag" from LETTER FROM A DISTANT LAND by Philip Booth, copyright 1956 by Philip Booth; for "River Skater" from BLOSSOMING ANTLERS by Winifred Welles, copyright 1933 by Winifred Welles.

Ann Wolfe for "The Grey Squirrel" by Humbert Wolfe.

5th printing .... September 1969

Printed in the U.S.A.

Acknowledgments

For advice and help we thank Exeter teachers who have tried out these poems in their classes – particularly Kenneth McElheny, Thomas Hinkle, Andrew Leaf, and Donald Thomas – and Exeter students who in recent years have contributed much to the selection of poems.

THE EDITORS

CONTENTS

Foreword

Cavalcade of Poems is constructed on the principle that Robert Frost expressed so well in the dedication of *You Come Too,* where he suggested that no poetry was good enough for young readers "that wasn't equally good for their elders." For years we have carried on with students a kind of conversation about poems. The poems in this book are partly the preference of students, partly our selection. The choices of students have had to meet the test of our interest, and our choices have had to catch the attention of the students.

The poems are arranged in eight groups, with the divisions of course slightly arbitrary and overlapping. Selection came, however, before grouping; every poem is in the book on its own merit.

A poem belongs to the reader, provided the reader is willing to listen to the poet. Discovery may come on the first reading, or the twenty-first.

George Bennett
Paul Molloy

Phillips Exeter Academy
Exeter, New Hampshire

GROUP 1
POEMS OF OBSERVATION

The Barley Field

Bent down by the rain,
the ripe barley makes this
such a narrow lane!

Joso

The Barley Field

Up the barley rows,
stitching, stitching them together
a butterfly goes.

Sora

Stubble

It has rained enough
To turn the stubble in the field
Black.

Basho

Umbrella

As I walk in the winter rain,
The umbrella
Pushes me back.

Shisei-jo

Butterflies

Fallen petals rise
back to the branch—I watch:
oh . . . butterflies!

Moritake

Hail

In the abandoned boat
The hail
Bounces about.

Shiki

Crane's Legs

Patiently the crane fishes in the lake,
His long red legs shortened since the rains.

Basho

Garden

Mossbound and weatherworn, the boulders stand;
Around them flows a stream of silver sand.

Ho-O

Downpour

The downpour prickles on the pond, so sharp
It hits the heads of shallow-floating carp.

Shiki

Spring Rain

Spring rain:
An umbrella and a straw coat
Go chatting together.

Buson

Spring Day

The spring day closes,
Lingering
Where there is water.

Issa

Above the Dock

Above the quiet dock in midnight,
Tangled in the tall mast's corded height,
Hangs the moon. What seemed so far away
Is but a child's balloon, forgotten after play.

T. E. Hulme

Dust of Snow

The way a crow
Shook down on me
The dust of snow
From a hemlock tree

Has given my heart
A change of mood
And saved some part
Of a day I had rued.

Robert Frost

In a Vacant Lot

Teasel weeds
Breast high in goldenrod
And Queen Anne's lace,
Blackened and sered by winter's grime and dirt,
Stand like Russian peasants,
Clad in old worn smocks
And mangy fur hats.

Anna Ulen Engleman

Tall Nettles

Tall nettles cover up, as they have done
These many springs, the rusty harrow, the plough
Long worn out, and the roller made of stone:
Only the elm butt tops the nettles now.

This corner of the farmyard I like most:
As well as any bloom upon a flower
I like the dust on the nettles, never lost
Except to prove the sweetness of a shower.

Edward Thomas

Sea Gulls

A myriad of tiny boats
Sat, riding on the sea.
With sudden creaking cries they rose
And wheeled away from me.

Far, far they went, into the blue
Away beyond the shore,
But presently they settled down;
There were my boats once more.

Anna Ulen Engleman

Skaters

Under the plum-dark hills,
under the low gold sun
in green and blue and red
brightly the children skate
across the frozen stream
like figures in a dream.

Frances Frost

The Skaters

Black swallows swooping or gliding
In a flurry of entangled loops and curves;
The skaters skim over the frozen river.
And the grinding click of their skates
as they impinge upon the surface,
Is like the brushing together of thin
wing tips of silver.

John Gould Fletcher

The Red Wheelbarrow

so much depends
upon

a red wheel
barrow

glazed with rain
water

beside the white
chickens

William Carlos Williams

GROUP 2

LONGER POEMS OF OBSERVATION

The Heron

The heron stands in water where the swamp
Has deepened to the blackness of a pool,
Or balances with one leg on a hump
Of marsh grass heaped above a muskrat hole.

He walks the shallow with an antic grace.
The great feet break the ridges of the sand,
The long eye notes the minnow's hiding place.
His beak is quicker than a human hand.

He jerks a frog across his bony lip,
Then points his heavy bill above the wood.
The wide wings flap but once to lift him up.
A single ripple starts from where he stood.

Theodore Roethke

Parachutist

After jump, drop and somersault
with cords unraveling in skein,
chute rising in a puff more taut
than sail until it domes a cone
of cords hooked to a harnessed dot
twirling and suspended like a toy
wind-swung and puppeted in space,
he pendulums sideways down the sky.

Samuel Hazo

The Eagle

He clasps the crag with crooked hands;
Close to the sun in lonely lands,
Ringed with the azure world, he stands.

The wrinkled sea beneath him crawls;
He watches from his mountain walls,
And like a thunderbolt he falls.

Alfred Tennyson

The Snow

It sifts from leaden sieves,
It powders all the wood,
It fills with alabaster wool
The wrinkles of the road.

It makes an even face
Of mountain and of plain, —
Unbroken forehead from the east
Unto the east again.

It reaches to the fence,
It wraps it, rail by rail,
Till it is lost in fleeces;
It flings a crystal veil

On stump and stack and stem, —
The summer's empty room,
Acres of seams where harvests were,
Recordless, but for them.

It ruffles wrists of posts
As ankles of a queen, —
Then stills its artisans like ghosts,
Denying they have been.

Emily Dickinson

Boats at Night

How lovely is the sound of oars at night
    And unknown voices, borne through windless
        air,
From shadowy vessels floating out of sight
    Beyond the harbor lantern's broken glare
To those piled rocks that make on the dark wave
    Only a darker stain. The splashing oars
Slide softly on as in an echoing cave
    And with the whisper of the unseen shores
Mingle their music, till the bell of night
    Murmurs reverberations low and deep
That droop towards the land in swooning flight
    Like whispers from the lazy lips of sleep.
The oars grow faint. Below the cloud-dim hill
The shadows fade and now the bay is still.

Edward Shanks

River Skater

Bound to a boy's swift feet, hard blades of steel
Ring out a brutal rhythm from black ice.
A gawky skater with a godlike heel,
He cuts a clear and convolute device,
A foliated script, nor looks around
To see what letters twine where he has come,
But all delighted with the savage sound,
His body beats from such a solid drum,
He springs into a faster pace, and then,
Far down the pastures, paper-white and pure,
You see his figure slanted like a pen,
Writing his own and winter's signature.

Winifred Welles

Outer Drive

Heat of nightfall, and the heave and start,
Beside a quivering sleek trolley on the track,
Of a sudden snub-cabbed truck, trailerless,
Intense; like a bullhead bodiless it rockets
Just grazing past the green tan flank
Of the wincing public car, lit up with heads
Featured in the window squares, going
Straight and ironbound, by safety islands,
Down the flickering neon evening, home—

While the deathless disembodied bullhead of a
truck
Escapes: past stoplights raging, headlights
steaming,
Rips through city limits eating, eating,
Eating all the highway up to Albany.

Edwin Honig

The Runaway

Once when the snow of the year was beginning to
    fall,
We stopped by a mountain pasture to say,
    "Whose colt?"
A little Morgan had one forefoot on the wall,
The other curled at his breast. He dipped his head
And snorted at us. And then he had to bolt,
We heard the miniature thunder where he fled,
And we saw him, or thought we saw him, dim and
    gray,
Like a shadow against the curtain of falling flakes.
"I think the little fellow's afraid of the snow.
He isn't winter-broken. It isn't play
With the little fellow at all. He's running away.
I doubt if even his mother could tell him, 'Sakes,
It's only weather.' He'd think she didn't know!
Where is his mother? He can't be out alone."
And now he comes again with a clatter of stone
And mounts the wall again with whited eyes
And all his tail that isn't hair up straight.
He shudders his coat as if to throw off flies.
"Whoever it is that leaves him out so late,
When other creatures have gone to stall and bin,
Ought to be told to come and take him in."

Robert Frost

Brimming Water

Under my feet the moon
Glides along the river.
Near midnight, a gusty lantern
Shines in the heart of night.
Along the sandbars flocks
Of white egrets roost,
Each one clenched like a fist.
In the wake of my barge
The fish leap, cut the water,
And dive and splash.

Tu Fu

Silver

Slowly, silently, now the moon
Walks the night in her silver shoon;
This way, and that, she peers, and sees
Silver fruit upon silver trees;
One by one the casements catch
Her beams beneath the silvery thatch;
Couched in his kennel, like a log,
With paws of silver sleeps the dog;
From their shadowy cote the white breasts peep
Of doves in a silver-feathered sleep;
A harvest mouse goes scampering by,
With silver claws, and a silver eye;
And moveless fish in the water gleam,
By silver reeds in a silver stream.

Walter de la Mare

GROUP 3
NARRATIVE POEMS

How They Brought the Good News from Ghent to Aix

I sprang to the stirrup, and Joris, and he;
I galloped, Dirck galloped, we galloped all three;
"Good speed!" cried the watch, as the gate-bolts
undrew;
"Speed!" echoed the wall to us galloping through;
Behind shut the postern, the lights sank to rest,
And into the midnight we galloped abreast.

Not a word to each other; we kept the great pace
Neck by neck, stride by stride, never changing
our place;
I turned in my saddle and made its girths tight,
Then shortened each stirrup, and set the pique
right,
Rebuckled the cheek-strap, chained slacker the bit,
Nor galloped less steadily Roland a whit.

'Twas moonset at starting; but, while we drew near
Lokeren, the cocks crew, and twilight dawned
clear;
At Boom, a great yellow star came out to see;
At Düffeld, 'twas morning as plain as could be;
And from Mecheln church steeple we heard the
half chime,
So Joris broke silence with, "Yet there is time!"

At Aershot, up leaped of a sudden the sun,
And against him the cattle stood black every one,
To stare through the mist at us galloping past;
And I saw my stout galloper Roland at last,
With resolute shoulders, each butting away
The haze, as some bluff river headland its spray:

And his low head and crest, just one sharp ear
bent back
For my voice, and the other pricked out on his track;
And one eye's black intelligence — ever that glance
O'er its white edge at me, his own master, askance!
And the thick heavy spume flakes which aye and
anon
His fierce lips shook upwards in galloping on.

By Hasselt, Dirck groaned; and cried Joris, "Stay
spur!
Your Roos galloped bravely, the fault's not in her,
We'll remember at Aix" — for one heard the quick
wheeze
Of her chest, saw the stretched neck and staggering
knees,
And sunk tail, and horrible heave of the flank,
As down on her haunches she shuddered and sank.

So, we were left galloping, Joris and I,
Past Looz and past Tongres, no cloud in the sky;
The broad sun above laughed a pitiless laugh,
'Neath our feet broke the bright little stubble like
chaff;

Till over by Dalhem a dome spire sprang white,
And "Gallop," gasped Joris, "for Aix is in sight!

"How they'll greet us!" — and all in a moment his
roan
Rolled neck and croup over, lay dead as a stone;
And there was my Roland to bear the whole weight
Of the news which alone could save Aix from her
fate,
With his nostrils like pits full of blood to the brim,
And with circles of red for his eye-sockets' rim.

Then I cast loose my buffcoat, each holster let fall,
Shook off both my jackboots, let go belt and all,
Stood up in the stirrup, leaned, patted his ear,
Called my Roland his pet-name, my horse without
peer;
Clapped my hands, laughed and sang, any noise,
bad or good,
Till at length into Aix Roland galloped and stood.

And all I remember is, friends flocking round
As I sat with his head 'twixt my knees on the
ground;
And no voice but was praising this Roland of mine,
As I poured down his throat our last measure
of wine,
Which (the burgesses voted by common consent)
Was no more than his due who brought good news
from Ghent.

Robert Browning

The Charge of the Light Brigade

Half a league, half a league,
    Half a league onward,
All in the valley of Death
    Rode the six hundred.
"Forward, the Light Brigade!
Charge for the guns!" he said:
Into the valley of Death
    Rode the six hundred.

"Forward, the Light Brigade!"
Was there a man dismayed?
Not though the soldier knew
    Someone had blundered:
Theirs not to make reply,
Theirs not to reason why,
Theirs but to do and die:
Into the valley of Death
    Rode the six hundred.

Cannon to right of them,
Cannon to left of them,
Cannon in front of them
    Volleyed and thundered;
Stormed at with shot and shell,
Boldly they rode and well,
Into the jaws of Death,
Into the mouth of Hell
    Rode the six hundred.

Flashed all their sabres bare,
Flashed as they turned in air
Sabring the gunners there,
Charging an army, while
All the world wondered:
Plunged in the battery smoke
Right through the line they broke;
Cossack and Russian
Reeled from the sabre stroke
Shattered and sundered.
Then they rode back, but not,
Not the six hundred.

Cannon to right of them,
Cannon to left of them,
Cannon behind them
Volleyed and thundered;
Stormed at with shot and shell,
While horse and hero fell,
They that had fought so well
Came through the jaws of Death,
Back from the mouth of Hell,
All that was left of them,
Left of six hundred.

When can their glory fade?
O the wild charge they made!
All the world wondered.
Honor the charge they made!
Honor the Light Brigade,
Noble six hundred!

Alfred Tennyson

The Forsaken

I

Once in the winter
Out on a lake
In the heart of the north-land,
Far from the Fort
And far from the hunters,
A Chippewa woman
With her sick baby,
Crouched in the last hours
Of a great storm.
Frozen and hungry,
She fished through the ice
With a line of the twisted
Bark of the cedar,
And a rabbit-bone hook
Polished and barbed;
Fished with the bare hook
All through the wild day,
Fished and caught nothing;
While the young chieftain
Tugged at her breasts,
Or slept in the lacing
Of the warm tikanagan.
All the lake surface
Streamed with the hissing
Of millions of iceflakes
Hurled by the wind;
Behind her the round

Of a lonely island
Roared like a fire
With the voice of the storm
In the deeps of the cedars.
Valiant, unshaken,
She took of her own flesh,
Baited the fishhook,
Drew in a gray trout,
Drew in his fellows,
Heaped them beside her,
Dead in the snow.
Valiant, unshaken,
She faced the long distance,
Wolf-haunted and lonely,
Sure of her goal
And the life of her dear one:
Tramped for two days,
On the third in the morning,
Saw the strong bulk
Of the Fort by the river,
Saw the wood smoke
Hang soft in the spruces,
Heard the keen yelp
Of the ravenous huskies
Fighting for whitefish:
Then she had rest.

II

Years and years after,
When she was old and withered,

When her son was an old man
And his children filled with vigor,
They came in their northern tour on the verge
of winter,
To an island in a lonely lake.
There one night they camped, and on the morrow
Gathered their kettles and birch bark,
Their rabbit-skin robes and their mink traps,
Launched their canoes and slunk away
through the islands,
Left her alone forever,
Without a word of farewell,
Because she was old and useless,
Like a paddle broken and warped,
Or a pole that was splintered.
Then, without a sigh,
Valiant, unshaken,
She smoothed her dark locks under her kerchief,
Composed her shawl in state,
Then folded her hands ridged with sinews
and corded with veins,
Folded them across her breasts spent
with the nourishing of children,
Gazed at the sky past the tops of the cedars,
Saw two spangled nights arise out of the twilight,
Saw two days go by filled
with the tranquil sunshine,
Saw, without pain, or dread, or even
a moment of longing:
Then on the third great night there came
thronging and thronging

Millions of snowflakes out of a windless cloud;
They covered her close with a beautiful
crystal shroud,
Covered her deep and silent.
But in the frost of the dawn,
Up from the life below,
Rose a column of breath
Through a tiny cleft in the snow,
Fragile, delicately drawn,
Wavering with its own weakness,
In the wilderness a sign of the spirit,
Persisting still in the sight of the sun
Till day was done.
Then all light was gathered up by the hand of God
and hid in His breast,
Then there was born a silence deeper than silence,
Then she had rest.

Duncan Campbell Scott

A Runnable Stag

When the pods went pop on the broom, green broom,
And apples began to be golden-skinned,
We harbored a stag in the Priory coomb,
And we feathered his trail up-wind, up-wind,
We feathered his trail up-wind —
A stag of warrant, a stag, a stag,
A runnable stag, a kingly crop,
Brow, bay and tray and three on top,
A stag, a runnable stag.

Then the huntsman's horn rang yap, yap, yap,
And "Forwards" we heard the harborer shout;
But 'twas only a brocket that broke a gap
In the beechen underwood, driven out,
From the underwood antlered out
By warrant and might of the stag, the stag,
The runnable stag, whose lordly mind
Was bent on sleep, though beamed and tined
He stood, a runnable stag.

So we tufted the covert till afternoon
With Tinkerman's Pup and Bell-of-the-North;
And hunters were sulky and hounds out of tune
Before we tufted the right stag forth,
Before we tufted him forth,
The stag of warrant, the wily stag,
The runnable stag with his kingly crop,
Brow, bay and tray and three on top,
The royal and runnable stag.

It was Bell-of-the-North and Tinkerman's Pup
    That stuck to the scent till the copse was drawn.
"Tally ho! tally ho!" and the hunt was up,
    The tufters whipped and the pack laid on,
    The resolute pack laid on,
        And the stag of warrant away at last,
        The runnable stag, the same, the same,
        His hoofs on fire, his horns like flame,
        A stag, a runnable stag.

"Let your gelding be: if you check or chide
    He stumbles at once and you're out of the hunt;
For three hundred gentlemen, able to ride,
    On hunters accustomed to bear the brunt,
    Accustomed to bear the brunt,
        Are after the runnable stag, the stag,
        The runnable stag with his kingly crop,
        Brow, bay and tray and three on top,
        The right, the runnable stag."

By perilous paths in coomb and dell,
    The heather, the rocks, and the river bed,
The pace grew hot, for the scent lay well,
    And a runnable stag goes right ahead,
    The quarry went right ahead —
        Ahead, ahead, and fast and far;
        His antlered crest, his cloven hoof,
        Brow, bay and tray and three aloof,
        The stag, the runnable stag.

For a matter of twenty miles and more,
    By the densest hedge and the highest wall,

Through herds of bullocks he baffled the lore
Of harborer, huntsman, hounds and all,
Of harborer, hounds and all —
The stag of warrant, the wily stag,
For twenty miles, and five and five,
He ran, and he never was caught alive,
This stag, this runnable stag.

When he turned at bay in the leafy gloom,
In the emerald gloom where the brook ran deep,
He heard in the distance the rollers boom,
And he saw in a vision of peaceful sleep,
In a wonderful vision of sleep,
A stag of warrant, a stag, a stag,
A runnable stag in a jewelled bed,
Under the sheltering ocean dead,
A stag, a runnable stag.

So a fateful hope lit up his eye,
And he opened his nostrils wide again,
And he tossed his branching antlers high
As he headed the hunt down the Charlock glen,
As he raced down the echoing glen
For five miles more, the stag, the stag,
For twenty miles, and five and five,
Not to be caught now, dead or alive,
The stag, the runnable stag.

Three hundred gentlemen, able to ride,
Three hundred horses as gallant and free,
Beheld him escape on the evening tide,
Far out till he sank in the Severn Sea,

Till he sank in the depths of the sea —
    The stag, the buoyant stag, the stag
    That slept at last in a jewelled bed
    Under the sheltering ocean spread,
    The stag, the runnable stag.

John Davidson

The Listeners

"Is there anybody there?" said the Traveler,
Knocking on the moonlit door;
And his horse in the silence champed the grasses
Of the forest's ferny floor;
And a bird flew up out of the turret,
Above the Traveler's head:
And he smote upon the door again a second time;
"Is there anybody there?" he said.
But no one descended to the Traveler;
No head from the leaf-fringed sill
Leaned over and looked into his gray eyes,
Where he stood perplexed and still.
But only a host of phantom listeners
That dwelt in the lone house then
Stood listening in the quiet of the moonlight
To that voice from the world of men:
Stood thronging the faint moonbeams on the dark stair,
That goes down to the empty hall,
Hearkening in an air stirred and shaken
By the lonely Traveler's call.
And he felt in his heart their strangeness,
Their stillness answering his cry,
While his horse moved, cropping the dark turf,
'Neath the starred and leafy sky;
For he suddenly smote on the door, even
Louder, and lifted his head:—

"Tell them I came, and no one answered,
That I kept my word," he said.
Never the least stir made the listeners,
Though every word he spake
Fell echoing through the shadowiness of the still house
From the one man left awake:
Ay, they heard his foot upon the stirrup,
And the sound of iron on stone,
And how the silence surged softly backward,
When the plunging hoofs were gone.

Walter de la Mare

The Mouse That Gnawed the Oak Tree Down

The mouse that gnawed the oak tree down
Began his task in early life.
He kept so busy with his teeth
He had no time to take a wife.

He gnawed and gnawed through sun and rain
When the ambitious fit was on,
Then rested in the sawdust till
A month of idleness had gone.

He did not move about to hunt
The coteries of mousie men.
He was a snail-paced, stupid thing
Until he cared to gnaw again.

The mouse that gnawed the oak tree down
When that tough foe was at his feet —
Found in the stump no angel cake
Nor buttered bread, nor cheese nor meat —

The forest roof let in the sky.
"This light is worth the work," said he.
"I'll make this ancient swamp more light,"
And started on another tree.

Vachel Lindsay

The Fox

First lambs have come, late snowfall to the hill.
All day he watches, feeding on greed
till, stars in the April sky, he steals
shadowy down the valleyside, furtive wades
marsh myrtle and by screen of heather comes
where flocks graze. Trembling for quarry
he scans each plucking lamb, chooses, pauses
strong as a spell, then flashes to revelry.

The lambless ewe sputters down the slope.
Home over Bristly Ridge in one sweep
he covers the Glyders, then deviously to his deep
mountain den, safe down creviced drop
where no terrier dares.

On his morning round
death in wool embers is the shepherd's find.

Ian Serraillier

Eight O'Clock

He stood, and heard the steeple
    Sprinkle the quarters on the morning town.
One, two, three, four, to market-place and people
    It tossed them down.

Strapped, noosed, nighing his hour,
    He stood and counted them and cursed his luck:
And then the clock collected in the tower
    Its strength, and struck.

A. E. Housman

The Ballad of Red Fox

Yellow sun yellow
Sun yellow sun,
When, oh, when
Will red fox run?

When the hollow horn shall sound,
When the hunter lifts his gun
And liberates the wicked hound,
Then, oh, then shall red fox run.

Yellow sun yellow
Sun yellow sun,
Where, oh, where
Will red fox run?

Through meadows hot as sulphur,
Through forests cool as clay,
Through hedges crisp as morning
And grasses limp as day.

Yellow sky yellow
Sky yellow sky,
How, oh, how
Will red fox die?

With a bullet in his belly,
A dagger in his eye,
And blood upon his red red brush
Shall red fox die.

Melvin Walker LaFollette

GROUP 4
HEROIC POEMS

O Captain! My Captain!

O Captain! my Captain! our fearful trip is done,
The ship has weather'd every rack, the prize
we sought is won,
The port is near, the bells I hear, the people
all exulting,
While follow eyes the steady keel, the vessel
grim and daring;
But O heart! heart! heart!
O the bleeding drops of red,
Where on the deck my Captain lies,
Fallen cold and dead.

O Captain! my Captain! rise up and hear the bells;
Rise up—for you the flag is flung—for you
the bugle trills,
For you bouquets and ribbon'd wreaths—for you
the shores a-crowding.
For you they call, the swaying mass, their eager
faces turning;
Here, Captain! dear father!
This arm beneath your head!
It is some dream that on the deck
You've fallen cold and dead.

My Captain does not answer, his lips are pale
and still.
My father does not feel my arm, he has no
pulse nor will,

The ship is anchor'd safe and sound, its voyage
closed and done.
From fearful trip the victor ship comes in
with object won;
Exult O shores, and ring O bells!
But I with mournful tread,
Walk the deck my Captain lies,
Fallen cold and dead.

Walt Whitman

Nancy Hanks

If Nancy Hanks
Came back as a ghost,
Seeking news
Of what she loved most,
She'd ask first
"Where's my son?
What's happened to Abe?
What's he done?

"Poor little Abe,
Left all alone
Except for Tom
Who's a rolling stone;
He was only nine

The year I died;
I remember still
How hard he cried.

"Scraping along
In a little shack,
With hardly a shirt
To cover his back,
And a prairie wind
To blow him down
Or pinching times
If he went to town.

"You wouldn't know
About my son?
Did he grow tall?
Did he have fun?
Did he learn to read?
Did he get to town?
Do you know his name?
Did he get on?"

Stephen Vincent Benét

The Burial of Sir John Moore at Corunna

Not a drum was heard, not a funeral note,
    As his corse to the rampart we hurried;
Not a soldier discharged his farewell shot
    O'er the grave where our hero we buried.

We buried him darkly at dead of night,
    The sods with our bayonets turning;
By the struggling moonbeam's misty light
    And the lantern dimly burning.

No useless coffin enclosed his breast,
    Not in sheet or in shroud we wound him;
But he lay like a warrior taking his rest
    With his martial cloak around him.

Few and short were the prayers we said,
    And we spoke not a word of sorrow;
But we steadfastly gaz'd on the face that was dead,
    And we bitterly thought of the morrow.

We thought, as we hollow'd his narrow bed
    And smooth'd down his lonely pillow,
That the foe and the stranger would tread
        o'er his head,
    And we far away on the billow!

Lightly they'll talk of the spirit that's gone
And o'er his cold ashes upbraid him, —
But little he'll reck, if they let him sleep on
In the grave where a Briton has laid hi

But half of our heavy task was done
When the clock struck the hour for retiring:
And we heard the distant and random gun
That the foe was sullenly firing.

Slowly and sadly we laid him down,
From the field of his fame fresh and gory;
We carved not a line, and we raised not a stone —
But we left him alone in his glory.

Charles Wolfe

Old Ironsides

Ay, tear her tattered ensign down!
  Long has it waved on high,
And many an eye has danced to see
  That banner in the sky;
Beneath it rung the battle shout,
  And burst the cannon's roar;
The meteor of the ocean air
  Shall sweep the clouds no more!

Her deck, once red with heroes' blood,
  Where knelt the vanquished foe,
When winds were hurrying o'er the flood,
  And waves were white below,
No more shall feel the victor's tread,
  Or know the conquered knee;
The harpies of the shore shall pluck
  The eagle of the sea!

O better that her shattered hulk
  Should sink beneath the wave;
Her thunders shook the mighty deep,
  And there should be her grave;
Nail to the mast her holy flag,
  Set every threadbare sail,
And give her to the god of storms,
  The lightning and the gale!

Oliver Wendell Holmes

Concord Hymn

By the rude bridge that arched the flood,
    Their flag to April's breeze unfurled,
Here once the embattled farmers stood
    And fired the shot heard round the world.

The foe long since in silence slept;
    Alike the conqueror silent sleeps;
And Time the ruined bridge has swept
    Down the dark stream which seaward creeps.

On this green bank, by this soft stream,
    We set today a votive stone;
That memory may their deed redeem,
    When, like our sires, our sons are gone.

Spirit, that made those heroes dare
    To die, and leave their children free,
Bid Time and Nature gently spare
    The shaft we raise to them and thee.

Ralph Waldo Emerson

The Man He Killed

"Had he and I but met
By some old ancient inn,
We should have sat us down to wet
Right many a nipperkin!

"But ranged as infantry,
And staring face to face,
I shot at him as he at me,
And killed him in his place.

"I shot him dead because —
Because he was my foe,
Just so: my foe of course he was;
That's clear enough; although

"He thought he'd 'list, perhaps
Off-hand like — just as I —
Was out of work, had sold his traps —
No other reason why.

"Yes; quaint and curious war is!
You shoot a fellow down
You'd treat if met where any bar is,
Or help to half-a-crown."

Thomas Hardy

After Blenheim

It was a summer evening,
    Old Kaspar's work was done,
And he before his cottage door
    Was sitting in the sun,
And by him sported on the green
His little grandchild Wilhelmine.

She saw her brother Peterkin
    Roll something large and round,
Which he beside the rivulet
    In playing there had found;
He came to ask what he had found
That was so large, and smooth, and round.

Old Kaspar took it from the boy,
    Who stood expectant by;
And then the old man shook his head,
    And with a natural sigh,
" 'Tis some poor fellow's skull," said he,
"Who fell in the great victory.

"I find them in the garden,
    For there's many here about;
And often when I go to plow,
    The plowshare turns them out!
For many thousand men," said he,
"Were slain in that great victory."

"Now tell us what 'twas all about,"
    Young Peterkin, he cries;
And little Wilhelmine looks up
    With wonder-waiting eyes;
"Now tell us all about the war,
And what they fought each other for."

"It was the English," Kaspar said,
    "Who put the French to rout;
But what they fought each other for
    I could not well make out;
But everybody said," quoth he,
"That 'twas a famous victory.

"My father lived at Blenheim then,
    Yon little stream hard by;
They burnt his dwelling to the ground,
    And he was forced to fly;
So with his wife and child he fled,
Nor had he where to rest his head.

"With fire and sword the country round
    Was wasted far and wide,
And many a childing mother then,
    And new-born baby died;
But things like that, you know, must be
At every famous victory.

"They say it was a shocking sight
    After the field was won;

For many thousand bodies here
    Lay rotting in the sun;
But things like that, you know, must be
After a famous victory.

"Great praise the Duke of Marlb'ro' won,
    And our good Prince Eugene."
"Why, 'twas a very wicked thing!"
    Said little Wilhelmine.
"Nay . . . nay . . . my little girl," quoth he,
"It was a famous victory.

"And everybody praised the Duke
    Who this great fight did win."
"But what good came of it at last?"
    Quoth little Peterkin.
"Why, that I cannot tell," said he,
"But 'twas a famous victory."

Robert Southey

GROUP 5
POEMS OF EXPERIENCE

Daffodils

I wandered lonely as a cloud
    That floats on high o'er vales an
When all at once I saw a crowd,
    A host, of golden daffodils;
Beside the lake, beneath the trees,
Fluttering and dancing in the breeze.

Continuous as the stars that shine
    And twinkle on the Milky Way,
They stretched in never-ending line
    Along the margin of a bay:
Ten thousand saw I at a glance,
Tossing their heads in sprightly dance.

The waves beside them danced, but they
    Out-did the sparkling waves in glee:
A poet could not but be gay,
    In such a jocund company:
I gazed — and gazed — but little thought
What wealth the show to me had brought:

For oft, when on my couch I lie
    In vacant or in pensive mood,
They flash upon that inward eye
    Which is the bliss of solitude;
And then my heart with pleasure fills,
And dances with the daffodils.

William Wordsworth

Seaside Golf

How straight it flew, how long it flew,
    It clear'd the rutty track
And soaring, disappeared from view
    Beyond the bunker's back —
A glorious, sailing, bounding drive
That made me glad I was alive.

And down the fairway, far along
    It glowed a lonely white;
I played an iron sure and strong
    And clipp'd it out of sight,
And spite of grassy banks between
I knew I'd find it on the green.

And so I did. It lay content
    Two paces from the pin;
A steady putt and then it went
    Oh, most securely in.
The very turf rejoiced to see
That quite unprecedented three.

Ah! seaweed smells from sandy caves
    And thyme and mist in whiffs,
Incoming tide, Atlantic waves
    Slapping the sunny cliffs,
Lark song and sea sounds in the air
And splendor, splendor everywhere.

John Betjeman

The Country Bedroom

My room's a square and candle-lighted boat,
In the surrounding depths of night afloat.
My windows are the portholes, and the seas
The sound of rain on the dark apple trees.

Sea-monster-like beneath, an old horse blows
A snort of darkness from his sleeping nose,
Below, among drowned daisies. Far off, hark!
Far off, one owl amidst the waves of dark.

Frances Cornford

The Bronco That Would Not Be Broken

A little colt — bronco, loaned to the farm
To be broken in time without fury or harm,
Yet black crows flew past you, shouting alarm,
Calling "Beware," with lugubrious singing . . .
The butterflies there in the bush were romancing,
The smell of the grass caught your soul in a trance,
So why be a-fearing the spurs and the traces,
O bronco that would not be broken of dancing?

You were born with the pride of the lords great
    and olden
Who danced, through the ages, in corridors golden.
In all the wide farm-place the person most human.
You spoke out so plainly with squealing
    and capering,
With whinnying, snorting, contorting and prancing,
As you dodged your pursuers, looking askance,
With Greek-footed figures, and Parthenon paces,
O bronco that would not be broken of dancing.

The grasshoppers cheered. "Keep whirling,"
    they said.
The insolent sparrows called from the shed,
"If men will not laugh, make them wish
    they were dead."
But arch were your thoughts, all malice displacing,
Though the horse-killers came, with snake-whips
    advancing.

You bantered and cantered away your last chance.
And they scourged you, with Hell in their speech
and their faces,
O bronco that would not be broken of dancing.

"Nobody cares for you," rattled the crows,
As you dragged the whole reaper, next day, down
the rows.
The three mules held back, yet you danced
on your toes.
You pulled like a racer, and kept the mules chasing.
You tangled the harness with bright eyes
side-glancing,
While the drunk driver bled you — a pole
for a lance —
And the giant mules bit at you — keeping
their places,
O bronco that would not be broken of dancing.

In that last afternoon your boyish heart broke.
The hot wind came down like a sledge-hammer
stroke.
The blood-sucking flies to a rare feast awoke.
And they searched out your wounds, your death-
warrant tracing.
And the merciful men, their religion enhancing,
Stopped the red reaper, to give you a chance.
Then you died on the prairie, and scorned
all disgraces,
O bronco that would not be broken of dancing.

Vachel Lindsay

Shag

Under the slow heron,
flip tern, and swung gull,
six black shags run on
the water, each duck skull

filled with weathervane
thought. Toward east wind
they take off on the run,
splashing until the shag mind

tells spent feet to retract.
Then the seventh shag,
straggling, begins to react.
His head bobs. The fog

closing in, he raises
himself on gargoyle wings,
drops again, then rises
and runs as he bangs

the sea on all fours.
Slower, then faster, he skims
the dark fir shores.
Momentarily he seems

to join the first flight.
But he shoots away,
shag-like, his thoughts flat
black. All shags fly

low. Ornithologists know
more: the perhaps why
and improbable how
of shag flight. They

call them cormorants,
or latinize the North name.
I row slow in the dense
weather. This is Maine;

and I slap the split port oar
of my leaking skiff,
drifting among the fir
islands, the seabirds, as if

on vacation from knowledge:
six black shags, shagging;
August fog, me, a Maine ledge,
and the seventh shag, lagging.

Philip Booth

Memory of Lake Superior

I know a country of bright anonymous beaches
Where the sand may sleep unprinted till it is stone.
Granite grows loud among the hills and ditches
Of the blown water when the water is blown.

Up on the mountain the sky is everywhere,
The lake fallen hugely underfoot as if
Into the bottom of a well of air,
The island upon it little as a leaf.

The woods are dark with the rank lace of hemlock
    and pine,
Beech, birch, and balsam, and the shadows of these.
There are mushrooms, and thimbleberries sweeter
    than wine,
And a far noise of wind in the tops of the trees.

That country was all the knowledge I shall ever
    learn.
It was all the wisdom I shall ever have.
It was there I looked for the driftwood boughs that
    burn
In colors like a memory of the wave.

It was there I looked along the forest floor
For the gray feather of a grouse's wing.
It was there I learned to look for nothing more,
Looking into the sea-blue eyes of spring.

George Dillon

The Chalk Cliff

Blasted and bored and undermined
    By quarrying seas
Reared the erect chalk cliff with black flints
    lined.
    (Flints drop like nuts from trees
When the frost bites
The chalk on winter nights.)

Save for frail shade of jackdaw's flight
    No night was there,
But blue-skyed summer and a cliff so white
    It stood like frozen air;
Foot slipped on damp
Chalk where the limpets camp.

With only purple of sea-stock
    And jackdaw's shade
To mitigate that blazing height of chalk
    I stood like a soul strayed
In paradise
Hiding my blinded eyes.

Andrew Young

My Parents Kept Me From Children Who Were Rough

My parents kept me from children who were rough
Who threw words like stones and who wore torn clothes.
Their thighs showed through rags. They ran in the street
And climbed cliffs and stripped by the country streams.

I feared more than tigers their muscles like iron
Their jerking hands and their knees tight on my arms.
I feared the salt-coarse pointing of those boys
Who copied my lisp behind me on the road.

They were lithe, they sprang out behind hedges
Like dogs to bark at my world. They threw mud
While I looked the other way, pretending to smile.
I longed to forgive them, but they never smiled.

Stephen Spender

A Memory

Skipping flat pebbles over the dark pond —
One of yours flipped nine times before it sank —
We watched the ripples spread, round after round,
Until the circles broke against the bank.
We played until the sun set, and the dank
Mist, heavy with the spicy smell of fern,
Rose from the reeds and warned us to return.

Of lives that intersect, then go their way,
At last to lose themselves alone against
The shores of silence, our brief hours of play
Seem now the symbol: the bright memory fenced
With deep, oblivious forest, and condensed
Into one flash, one fragmentary scene
That skips the surface of the years between.

You had a decade left that afternoon
Before you were to die in the first war;
But deep within me, like a sealed cocoon,
The memory clung, for fifty years and more,
To open for one sudden flight and soar
Into this moment lost in time beyond
Two small boys skipping pebbles over the pond.

Robert Hillyer

The Fish

I caught a tremendous fish
and held him beside the boat
half out of water, with my hook
fast in a corner of his mouth.
He didn't fight.
He hadn't fought at all.
He hung a grunting weight,
battered and venerable
and homely. Here and there
his brown skin hung in strips
like ancient wall paper,
and its pattern of darker brown
was like wall paper:
shapes like full-blown roses
stained and lost through age.
He was speckled with barnacles,
fine rosettes of lime,
and infested
with tiny white sea-lice,
and underneath two or three
rags of green weed hung down.
While his gills were breathing in
the terrible oxygen
— the frightening gills
fresh and crisp with blood,
that can cut so badly —
I thought of the coarse white flesh
packed in like feathers,
the big bones and the little bones,

the dramatic reds and blacks
of his shiny entrails,
and the pink swim-bladder
like a big peony.
I looked into his eyes
which were far larger than mine
but shallower, and yellowed,
the irises backed and packed
with tarnished tinfoil
seen through the lenses
of old scratched isinglass.
They shifted a little, but not
to return my stare.
—It was more like the tipping
of an object toward the light.
I admired his sullen face,
the mechanism of his jaw,
and then I saw
that from his lower lip
— if you could call it a lip —
grim, wet, and weapon-like,
hung five old pieces of fish-line,
or four and a wire leader
with the swivel still attached,
with all their five big hooks
grown firmly in his mouth.
A green line, frayed at the end
where he broke it, two heavier lines,
and a fine black thread
still crimped from the strain and snap
when it broke and he got away.
Like medals with their ribbons

frayed and wavering,
a five-haired beard of wisdom
trailing from his aching jaw.
I stared and stared
and victory filled up
the little rented boat,
from the pool of bilge
where oil had spread a rainbow
around the rusted engine
to the boiler rusted orange
the sun-cracked thwarts,
the oarlocks on their strings,
the gunnels — until everything
was rainbow, rainbow, rainbow!
And I let the fish go.

Elizabeth Bishop

That Dark Other Mountain

My father could go down a mountain faster than I
Though I was first one up.
Legs braced or with quick steps he slid
  the gravel slopes
Where I picked cautious footholds.

Black, Iron, Eagle, Doublehead, Chocorua,
Wildcat and Carter Dome —
He beat me down them all. And that last
  other mountain,
And that dark other mountain.

Robert Francis

GROUP 6

POEMS IN PAIRS FOR COMPARISON

A Noiseless Patient Spider

A noiseless patient spider,
I mark'd where on a little promontory it stood
isolated,
Mark'd how to explore the vacant vast surrounding,
It launch'd forth filament, filament, filament,
out of itself.
Ever unreeling them, ever tirelessly speeding them.

And you O my soul where you stand,
Surrounded, detached, in measureless oceans
of space,
Ceaselessly musing, venturing, throwing, seeking
the spheres to connect them.
Till the bridge you will need be form'd, till
the ductile anchor hold,
Till the gossamer thread you fling catch somewhere,
O my soul.

Walt Whitman

The Chambered Nautilus

This is the ship of pearl, which, poets feign,
    Sails the unshadowed main, —
    The venturous bark that flings
On the sweet summer wind its purpled wings
In gulfs enchanted, where the siren sings,
    And coral reefs lie bare,
Where the cold sea-maids rise to sun their streaming
        hair.

Its webs of living gauze no more unfurl;
    Wrecked is the ship of pearl!
    And every chambered cell,
Where its dim dreaming life was wont to dwell,
As the frail tenant shaped his growing shell
    Before thee lies revealed, —
Its irised ceiling rent, its sunless crypt unsealed!

Year after year behold the silent toil
    That spread his lustrous coil;
    Still, as the spiral grew,
He left the past year's dwelling for the new,
Stole with soft step its shining archway through,
    Built up its idle door,
Stretched in his last-found home, and knew the old
        no more.

Thanks for the heavenly message brought by thee,
    Child of the wandering sea,
    Cast from her lap forlorn!
From thy dead lips a clearer note is born

Than ever Triton blew from wreathèd horn!
While on mine ear it rings,
Through the deep caves of thought I hear a voice
that sings: —

Build thee more stately mansions, O my soul,
As the swift seasons roll!
Leave thy low-vaulted past!
Let each new temple, nobler than the last,
Shut thee from heaven with a dome more vast,
Till thou at length art free,
Leaving thine outgrown shell by life's unresting sea.

Oliver Wendell Holmes

An Epitaph

Here lies a most beautiful lady,
Light of step and heart was she;
I think she was the most beautiful lady
That ever was in the West Country.

But beauty vanishes; beauty passes;
However rare — rare it be;
And when I crumble, who will remember
This lady of the West Country?

Walter de la Mare

Annabel Lee

It was many and many a year ago,
In a kingdom by the sea,
That a maiden there lived whom you may know
By the name of Annabel Lee.
And this maiden lived with no other thought
Than to love and be loved by me.

I was a child and she was a child
In this kingdom by the sea:
But we loved with a love that was more than love —
I and my Annabel Lee,
With a love that the winged seraphs of heaven
Coveted her and me.

And this was the reason that, long ago,
In this kingdom by the sea,
A wind blew out of a cloud, chilling
My beautiful Annabel Lee,
So that her high-born kinsmen came
And bore her away from me,
To shut her up in a sepulchre
In this kingdom by the sea.

The angels, not half so happy in heaven,
Went envying her and me —
Yes! that was the reason (as all men know,
In this kingdom by the sea)
That the wind came out of the cloud one night,
Chilling and killing my Annabel Lee.

But our love it was stronger by far than the love
Of those who were older than we —
Of many far wiser than we —
And neither the angels in heaven above,
Nor the demons down under the sea,
Can ever dissever my soul from the soul
Of the beautiful Annabel Lee.

For the moon never beams without bringing me dreams
Of the beautiful Annabel Lee;
And the stars never rise, but I feel the bright eyes
Of the beautiful Annabel Lee;
And so, all the night-tide, I lie down by the side
Of my darling — my darling — my life and my bride,
In the sepulchre there by the sea,
In her tomb by the sounding sea.

Edgar Allan Poe

Under a Telephone Pole

I am a copper wire slung in the air,
Slim against the sun I make not even a clear line
    of shadow.
Night and day I keep singing — humming
    and thrumming;
It is love and war and money; it is the fighting
    and the tears, the work and want,
Death and laughter of men and women passing
    through me, carrier of your speech,
In the rain and the wet dripping, in the dawn
    and the shine drying,
A copper wire.

Carl Sandburg

The Line-Gang

Here come the line-gang pioneering by.
They throw a forest down less cut than broken.
They plant dead trees for living, and the dead
They string together with a living thread.
They string an instrument against the sky
Wherein words whether beaten out or spoken
Will run as hushed as when they were a thought.
But in no hush they string it: they go past
With shouts afar to pull the cable taut,
To hold it hard until they make it fast,
To ease away — they have it. With a laugh,
An oath of towns that set the wild at naught
They bring the telephone and telegraph.

Robert Frost

The Moth and the Lamp

The moth,
Enraged,
Beats against the lamp,
His wings forming
Countless tiny fans,
And falls at last
A fragile pinch of gray ashes.
The lamp burns on,
Tranquilly.

Paul Eldridge

The Moth

Isled in the midnight air,
Musked with the dark's faint bloom,
Out into glooming and secret haunts
        The flame cries, "Come!"

Lovely in dye and fan,
A-tremble in shimmering grace,
A moth from her winter swoon
        Uplifts her face:

Stares from her glamorous eyes;
Wafts her on plumes like mist;
In ecstasy swirls and sways
        To her strange tryst.

Walter de la Mare

Cargoes

Quinquireme of Nineveh from distant Ophir,
Rowing home to haven in sunny Palestine,
With a cargo of ivory,
And apes and peacocks,
Sandalwood, cedarwood, and sweet white wine.

Stately Spanish galleon coming from the Isthmus,
Dipping through the Tropics by the palm-green
shores,
With a cargo of diamonds,
Emeralds, amethysts,
Topazes, and cinnamon, and gold moidores.

Dirty British coaster with a salt-caked smoke stack,
Butting through the Channel in the mad March days,
With a cargo of Tyne coal,
Road rails, pig lead,
Firewood, iron ware, and cheap tin trays.

John Masefield

The Old Ships

I have seen old ships sail like swans asleep
Beyond the village which men still call Tyre
With leaden age o'ercargoed, dipping deep
For Famagusta and the hidden sun

That rings black Cyprus with a lake of fire;
And all those ships were certainly so old —
Who knows how oft with squat and noisy gun,
Questing brown slaves or Syrian oranges,
The pirate Genoese
Hell-raked them till they rolled
Blood, water, fruit and corpses up the hold.
But now through friendly seas they softly run,
Painted the mid-sea blue or shore-sea green,
Still patterned with the vine and grapes in gold.

But, I have seen,
Pointing her shapely shadows from the dawn
And image tumbled on a rose-swept bay,
A drowsy ship of some yet older day;
And, wonder's breath indrawn,
Thought I — who knows — who knows — but in
  that same
(Fished up beyond Æaea, patched up new
— Stern painted brighter blue —)
That talkative bald-headed seaman came
(Twelve patient comrades sweating at the oar)
From Troy's doom-crimson shore,
And with great lies about his wooden horse
Set the crew laughing, and forgot his course.

It was so old a ship — who knows, who knows?
— And yet so beautiful, I watched in vain
To see the mast burst open with a rose,
And the whole deck put on its leaves again.

James Elroy Flecker

A Narrow Fellow in the Grass

A narrow fellow in the grass
Occasionally rides;
You may have met him,—did you not?
His notice sudden is.

The grass divides as with a comb,
A spotted shaft is seen;
And then it closes at your feet
And opens further on.

He likes a boggy acre,
A floor too cool for corn.
Yet when a child, and barefoot,
I more than once, at morn,

Have passed, I thought, a whip lash
Unbraiding in the sun,—
When, stooping to secure it,
It wrinkled, and was gone.

Several of nature's people
I know, and they know me;
I feel for them a transport
Of cordiality;

But never met this fellow,
Attended or alone,
Without a tighter breathing,
And zero at the bone.

Emily Dickinson

Snake

A snake! Though it passes,
eyes that had glared at me
stay in the grasses.

Kyoshi

Crystal Moment

Once or twice this side of death
Things can make one hold his breath.

From my boyhood I remember
A crystal moment of September.

A wooded island rang with sounds
Of church bells in the throats of hounds.

A buck leaped out and took the tide
With jewels flowing past each side.

With his high head like a tree
He swam within a yard of me.

I saw the golden drop of light
In his eyes turned dark with fright.

I saw the forest's holiness
On him like a fierce caress.

Fear made him lovely past belief,
My heart was trembling like a leaf.

He leaned towards the land and life
With need above him like a knife.

In his wake the hot hounds churned,
They stretched their muzzles out and yearned.

They bayed no more, but swam and throbbed,
Hunger drove them till they sobbed.

Pursued, pursuers reached the shore
And vanished. I saw nothing more.

So they passed, a pageant such
As only gods could witness much,

Life and death upon one tether
And running beautiful together.

Robert P. Tristram Coffin

The Buck in the Snow

White sky, over the hemlocks bowed with snow,
Saw you not at the beginning of evening the antlered
    buck and his doe
Standing in the apple orchard? I saw them. I saw
    them suddenly go,
Tails up, with long leaps lovely and slow,
Over the stone wall into the woods of hemlocks
    bowed with snow.

Now lies he here, his wild blood scalding the snow.

How strange a thing is death, bringing to his knees,
    bringing to his antlers
The buck in the snow.
How strange a thing, a mile away by now, it may be,
Under the heavy hemlocks, that as the moments
    pass,
Shift their loads a little, letting fall a feather
    of snow —
Life, looking out attentive from the eyes
    of the doe.

Edna St. Vincent Millay

Ozymandias

I met a traveler from an antique land
Who said: Two vast and trunkless legs of stone
Stand in the desert. Near them, on the sand,
Half sunk, a shattered visage lies, whose frown,
And wrinkled lip, and sneer of cold command,
Tell that its sculptor well those passions read
Which yet survive, stamped on these lifeless things,
The hand that mocked them, and the heart that fed.
And on the pedestal these words appear:
"My name is Ozymandias, king of kings:
Look on my works, ye Mighty, and despair!"
Nothing beside remains. Round the decay
Of that colossal wreck, boundless and bare
The lone and level sands stretch far away.

Percy Bysshe Shelley

The Hammers

Noise of hammers once I heard
Many hammers, busy hammers,
Beating, shaping night and day,
Shaping, beating dust and clay
To a palace; saw it reared;
Saw the hammers laid away.

And I listened, and I heard
Hammers beating, night and day
In the palace newly reared,
Beating it to dust and clay:
Other hammers, muffled hammers,
Silent hammers of decay.

Ralph Hodgson

Manhole Covers

The beauty of manhole covers — what of that?
Like medals struck by a great savage khan,
Like Mayan calendar stones, unliftable,
  indecipherable,
Not like old electrum, chased and scored,
Mottoed and sculptured to a turn,
But notched and whelked and pocked and smashed
With the great company names:
Gentle Bethlehem, smiling United States.
This rustproof artifact of my street,
Long after roads are melted away, will lie
Sidewise in the grave of the iron-old world,
Bitten at the edges,
Strong with its cryptic American,
Its dated beauty.

Karl Shapiro

Pelicans

Four pelicans went over the house,
Sculled their worn oars over the courtyard:
    I saw that ungainliness
Magnifies the idea of strength.
A lifting gale of sea-gulls followed them;
    slim yachts of the element,
Natural growths of the sky, no wonder
Light wings to leave sea; but those grave weights
    toil, and are powerful,
And the wings torn with old storms remember
The cone that the oldest redwood dropped from,
    the tilting of continents,
The dinosaur's day, the life of new sea-lines.
The omnisecular spirit keeps the old
    with the new also.
Nothing at all has suffered erasure.
There is life not of our time. He calls
    ungainly bodies
As beautiful as the grace of horses.
He is weary of nothing; he watches airplanes,
    he watches pelicans.

Robinson Jeffers

Blue-Butterfly Day

It is blue-butterfly day here in spring,
And with these sky-flakes down in flurry on flurry
There is more unmixed color on the wing
Than flowers will show for days unless they hurry.

But these are flowers that fly and all but sing:
And now from having ridden out desire
They lie closed over in the wind and cling
Where wheels have freshly sliced the April mire.

Robert Frost

Chanson Innocent

in Just-
spring   when the world is mud-
luscious the little
lame balloonman

whistles   far   and wee

and eddieandbill come
running from marbles and
piracies and it's
spring

when the world is puddle-wonderful

the queer
old balloonman whistles
far   and   wee
and bettyandisbel come dancing

from hop-scotch and jump-rope and

it's
spring
and
   the
      goat-footed

balloonMan   whistles
far
and
wee

E. E. Cummings

GROUP 7
POEMS OF THE CHALLENGE OF LIFE

Written on the Eve of Execution

My prime of youth is but a frost of cares,
  My feast of joy is but a dish of pain,
My crop of corn is but a field of tares,
  And all my good is but vain hope of gain;
My life is fled, and yet I saw no sun;
And now I live, and now my life is done.

My tale was heard, and yet it was not told;
  My fruit is fallen, and yet my leaves are green;
My youth is spent, and yet I am not old;
  I saw the world, and yet I was not seen;
My thread is cut, and yet it is not spun;
And now I live, and now my life is done.

I sought my death and found it in the womb,
  I looked for life and saw it was a shade,
I trod the earth and knew it was my tomb,
  And now I die, and now I was but made;
My glass is full, and now my glass is run,
And now I live, and now my life is done.

Chidiock Tichborne

Requiem

Under the wide and starry sky,
Dig the grave and let me lie.
Glad did I live and gladly die,
    And I laid me down with a will.

This be the verse you grave for me:
Here he lies where he longed to be,
Home is the sailor, home from the sea,
    And the hunter home from the hill.

Robert Louis Stevenson

The Wayfarer

The wayfarer,
Perceiving the pathway to truth,
Was struck with astonishment.
It was thickly grown with weeds.
"Ha," he said,
"I see that no one has passed here
In a long time."
Later he saw that each weed
Was a singular knife.
"Well," he mumbled at last,
"Doubtless there are other roads."

Stephen Crane

I Saw a Man

I saw a man pursuing the horizon;
Round and round they sped.
I was disturbed at this;
I accosted the man.
"It is futile," I said,
"You can never" —

"You lie," he cried,
And ran on.

Stephen Crane

The Victim

The hummingbird that darts and hovers
Made one fatal dart — alas! —
Against a counterfeit of flowers
Reflected in the window glass.
When four-o'clocks had sunk in shadow,
The window caught an extra glint
Of color, like the sudden rainbow
Arching the purple firmament.
Transcendent are the traceries
Illusion weaves to set a snare;
The quick competitor of bees,
Trusting his universe of air
For flight and honey, dazzled so
In quest of sweetness, was waylaid
By something hard that had a glow
Brighter than that the garden made.
Illusion shatters; the ideal
Is much more ruthless than the real.
The visionary hummingbird
Hit nothingness, and hit it hard.

Robert Hillyer

Reveille

Wake: the silver dusk returning
    Up the beach of darkness brims,
And the ship of sunrise burning
    Strands upon the eastern rims.

Wake: the vaulted shadow shatters,
    Trampled to the floor it spanned.
And the tent of night in tatters
    Straws the sky-pavilioned land.

Up, lad, up, 'tis late for lying:
    Hear the drums of morning play;
Hark, the empty highways crying
    "Who'll beyond the hills away?"

Towns and countries woo together,
    Forelands beacon, belfries call;
Never lad that trod on leather
    Lived to feast his heart with all.

Up, lad: thews that lie and cumber
    Sunlit pallets never thrive;
Morns abed and daylight slumber
    Were not meant for man alive.

Clay lies still, but blood's a rover:
    Breath's a ware that will not keep.
Up, lad: when the journey's over
    There'll be time enough to sleep.

A. E. Housman

Crossing the Bar

Sunset and evening star,
  And one clear call for me!
And may there be no moaning of the bar,
  When I put out to sea,

But such a tide as moving seems asleep,
  Too full for sound and foam,
When that which drew from out the boundless deep
  Turns again home.

Twilight and evening bell,
  And after that the dark!
And may there be no sadness of farewell,
  When I embark;

For tho' from out our bourn of Time and Place
  The flood may bear me far,
I hope to see my Pilot face to face
  When I have crossed the bar.

Alfred Tennyson

GROUP 8

A RANGE BEYOND

Deer

Shy in their herding dwell the fallow deer.
They are spirits of wild sense. Nobody near
Comes upon their pastures. There a life they live,
Of sufficient beauty, phantom, fugitive,
Treading as in jungles free leopards do,
Printless as eyelight, instant as dew.
The great kine are patient, and homecoming sheep
Know our bidding. The fallow deer keep
Delicate and far their counsels wild,
Never to be folded reconciled
To the spoiling hand as the poor flocks are;
Lightfoot, and swift, and unfamiliar,
These you may not hinder, unconfined
Beautiful flocks of the mind.

John Drinkwater

The Grey Squirrel

Like a small grey
coffee pot
sits the squirrel.
He is not

all he should be,
kills by dozens
trees, and eats
his red-brown cousins.

The keeper, on the
other hand
, who shot him, is
a Christian, and

loves his enemies,
which shows
the squirrel was not
one of those.

Humbert Wolfe

August

Why should this Negro insolently stride
Down the red noonday on such noiseless feet?
Piled in his barrow, tawnier than wheat,
Lie heaps of smoldering daisies, somber-eyed,
Their copper petals shriveled up with pride,
Hot with a superfluity of heat,
Like a great brazier borne along the street
By captive leopards, black and burning pied.

Are there no water lilies, smooth as cream,
With long stems dripping crystal? Are there none
Like those white lilies, luminous and cool,
Plucked from some hemlock-darkened northern
stream
By fair-haired swimmers, diving where the sun
Scarce warms the surface of the deepest pool?

Elinor Wylie

The Hunchback in the Park

The hunchback in the park
A solitary mister
Propped between trees and water
From the opening of the garden lock
That let the trees and water enter
Until the Sunday somber bell at dark,

Eating bread from a newspaper
Drinking water from the chained cup
That the children filled with gravel
In the fountain basin where I sailed my ship
Slept at night in a dog kennel
But nobody chained him up.

Like the park birds he came early
Like the water he sat down
And Mister they called hey Mister
The truant boys from the town
Running when he had heard them clearly
On out of sound

Past lake and rockery
Laughing when he shook his paper
Hunchbacked in mockery
Through the loud zoo of the willow groves
Dodging the park keeper
With his stick that picked up leaves.

And the old dog sleeper
Alone between nurses and swans
While the boys among willows
Made the tiger jump out of their eyes
To roar on the rockery stones
And the groves were blue with sailors

Made all day until bell time
A woman figure without fault
Straight as a young elm
Straight and tall from his crooked bones
That she might stand in the night
After the lock and chains

All night in the unmade park
After the railings and shrubberies
The birds the grass the trees the lake
Had followed the hunchback
And the wild boys innocent as strawberries
To his kennel in the dark.

Dylan Thomas

Boy at the Window

Seeing the snowman standing all alone
In dusk and cold is more than he can bear.
The small boy weeps to hear the wind prepare
A night of gnashings and enormous moan.
His tearful sight can hardly reach to where
The pale-faced figure with bitumen eyes
Returns him such a god-forsaken stare
As outcast Adam gave to Paradise.

The man of snow is, nonetheless, content,
Having no wish to go inside and die.
Still, he is moved to see the youngster cry.
Though frozen water is his element,
He melts enough to drop from one soft eye
A trickle of the purest rain, a tear
For the child at the bright pane surrounded by
Such warmth, such light, such love,
    and so much fear.

Richard Wilbur

Pastoral

The wise old apple tree in spring,
Though split and hollow, makes a crown
Of such fantastic blossoming
We cannot let them cut it down.
It bears no fruit, but honey bees
Prefer it to the other trees.

The orchard man chalks his mark
And says, "This empty shell must go."
We nod and rub it off the bark
As soon as he goes down the row.
Each spring he looks bewildered. "Queer,
I thought I marked this thing last year."

Ten orchard men have come and gone
Since first I saw my grandfather
Slyly erase it. I'm the one
To do it now. As I defer
The showy veteran's removal
My grandson nods his full approval.

Like mine, my fellow ancient's roots
Are deep in the last century
From which our memories send shoots
For all our grandchildren to see
How spring, inviting bloom and rhyme,
Defeats the orchard men of time.

Robert Hillyer

Evening Ebb

The ocean has not been so quiet for a long while;
    five night-herons
Fly shorelong voiceless in the hush of the air
Over the calm of an ebb that almost mirrors their
    wings.
The sun has gone down, and the water has gone
    down
From the weed-clad rock, but the distant
    cloud-wall rises. The ebb whispers.
Great cloud-shadows float in the opal water.
Through rifts in the screen of the world
    pale gold gleams, and the evening
Star suddenly glides like a flying torch.
As if we had not been meant to see her;
    rehearsing behind
The screen of the world for another audience.

Robinson Jeffers

The Dark Hills

Dark hills at evening in the west,
Where sunset hovers like a sound
Of golden horns that sang to rest
Old bones of warriors under ground,
Far now from all the bannered ways
Where flash the legions of the sun,
You fade — as if the last of days
Were fading, and all wars were done.

Edwin Arlington Robinson

Questioning Faces

The winter owl banked just in time to pass
And save herself from breaking window glass.
And her wings straining suddenly aspread
Caught color from the last of evening red
In a display of underdown and quill
To glassed-in children at the window sill.

Robert Frost

Notes

Group 1

The poems from "The Barley Field" through "Spring Day" are translations of a type of Japanese poem named "haiku." In translation the subtlety and suggestiveness of the originals are lost, but we can at least appreciate the skill of the poets in bringing the ordinary, everyday things of life before us in a fresh way or in a new relationship. In Japanese, the haiku contains exactly seventeen syllables; translators try to match the conciseness of the original.

Garden. This poem is about the Garden of Ryoan in Kyoto, which dates from 1469. The whole garden consists of the boulders and the carefully raked sand.

Spring Rain. In *An Introduction to Haiku,* H. C. Henderson points out that the "straw raincoat would be worn by a man and the umbrella used by a woman." We recommend this book (a Doubleday Anchor paperback) for further reading.

Dust of Snow. *rued*: regretted.

The Red Wheelbarrow. Doctor Williams, who practiced medicine at Rutherford, N. J., for many years, wrote this comment for *Fifty Poets,* ed. by Wm. Rose Benét: "The wheelbarrow in question stood outside the window of an old Negro's house on a back street in the suburb where I live. It was pouring rain and there were white chickens walking about in it. The sight impressed me somehow as about the most important, the most integral, that it had ever been my pleasure to gaze upon."

Group 2

River Skater. *a godlike heel*: the winged foot of the god Mercury.

The Runaway. *a little Morgan*: a small horse first bred in Vermont not many miles from the poet's farm in Ripton.

Silver. *shoon*: archaic plural for shoes.

cote: dovecote, a house for doves and pigeons.

silver: notice the repetition of this word.

Group 3

How They Brought the Good News from Ghent to Aix. Browning wrote on Jan. 23, 1881: "There is no sort of historical foundation about 'Good News [from] Ghent.' I wrote it under the bulwark of a vessel, off the African coast, after I had been at sea long enough to appreciate even the fancy of a gallop on the back of a certain good horse 'York,' then in my stable at home." In another letter Browning writes: "there is no historical incident whatever commemorated by the poem you mention—a merely general impression of the characteristic warfare and besieging which abound in the annals of Flanders. This accounts for some of the difficulties in the time and space occupied by the ride in one night." Browning had twice been through Flanders (in 1834 and 1838) and, writing from memory, he made the riders travel very indirectly to Aix and cover over 120 miles.

Aix: Aix-la-Chapelle (also called Aachen), a town in western Germany about 100 miles from Ghent in Belgium. Aix was the capital of Charlemagne's empire and coronation city (813-1531) of the Holy Roman Empire.

pique: mistakenly used by the poet for *peak* (the pommel of the saddle).

The Charge of the Light Brigade. During the Crimean War, on October 25, 1854, British cavalry, through an error of the command, charged straight at the Russian field batteries on the heights of Balaklava (seaport on the Black Sea), meeting a deadly converging gunfire. Two thirds of the "Light Brigade" fell on the field of battle.

The Forsaken. *the Fort*: a trading post.

tikanagan: a kind of Indian cradle into which an infant was laced and thus carried on the mother's back.

A Runnable Stag. *a stag of warrant*: a stag old enough (5 or 6 years) to be hunted legally.

The Fox. *late snowfall to the hill*: lambs like patches of snow on the hillside.

plucking: tugging at the mother.

flashes to revelry: speed, color, feasting.

strong as a spell: the fox poised and certain as if he held the lamb under an enchantment.

death in wool embers: since *embers* means burning coals, the suggestion is of blood on the scattered bits of fur.

Eight O'Clock. *Sprinkle the quarters*: chiming of the quarter hours.

Group 4

O Captain! My Captain! Walt Whitman wrote this poem in 1865, the year of Lincoln's assassination.

The Burial of Sir John Moore at Corunna. Sir John Moore died in January, 1809, after a victorious skirmish with the French at Corunna, a fortified city on the northwestern coast of Spain, and was buried before dawn in the ramparts. He was called the finest trainer of men the British army had ever known.

Old Ironsides. The nickname was given to the U.S. frigate *Constitution* because of the way she stood up under fire. Built in 1797, she is best remembered for her victory over the British man-of-war *Guerriére* in the War of 1812. When in 1828 the Navy Department gave orders that she was to be dismantled, Holmes, then a young medical student, responded by writing "Old Ironsides." The poem was reprinted in the papers all over the country and aroused so much feeling that the Navy's orders were canceled. Later the public subscribed enough money to repair the ship. It is now a national monument at a dock in the Charlestown, Mass., Navy yard.

harpies: In classical mythology the harpies were foul, malign creatures, part woman, part bird, that snatched away the souls of the dead or seized or defiled the food of their victims.

The Man He Killed. *nipperkin*: a measure for liquor, containing half a pint or less.

traps: belongings or gear.

After Blenheim. Blenheim, a village of Bavaria, Germany, was the scene of a decisive victory by the English and Austrians over French and Bavarian forces (War of the Spanish Succession, 1702–1713). The battle took place August 13, 1704. The Austrians were commanded by Prince Eugene and the English by the famous Duke of Marlborough.

Group 5

The Bronco That Would Not Be Broken. *Parthenon paces*: resembling the unharnessed horses in the dynamic sculptures which adorned the pediments of the Parthenon, the Doric temple of Athena built on the Acropolis in Athens in the 5th century B.C. The fragments of these pediments are part of the Elgin Marbles, and since 1816 they have been in the British Museum. Excellent photographs of the Elgin Marbles appeared in *Life* magazine, October 26, 1953.

Shag. *raises himself on gargoyle wings*: shags cannot fly when their wings are soaked with sea water; they must perch and spread their wings like the mythological creatures carved in stone that serve as waterspouts on medieval cathedrals.

latinize the North name: the English word *shag* is like the Old Norse *skegg,* meaning beard, perhaps with reference to the bird's shaggy crest. The word *cormorant* is derived from the Latin *corvus marinus,* meaning sea raven.

That Dark Other Mountain. *Black, Iron, Eagle,* etc.: the mountains are in the White Mountains of New Hampshire.

Group 6

The Chambered Nautilus. The nautilus, a mollusk or shellfish, occupies successively larger chambers as its spiral shell grows.

its purpled wings: the tentacles with which the nautilus obtains its food were once thought to be wings.

An Epitaph. *the West Country*: the southwestern counties (Somerset, Devon, etc.) of England.

The Moth. *tryst*: an appointed place of meeting.

Cargoes. *Quinquireme*: ancient ship having five banks of oars.

Nineveh: capital city of the Assyrian Empire (about 750-612 B.C.).

moidores: an obsolete Portuguese gold coin.

galleon: sailing vessel of the 15th and following centuries, often having three or four decks.

Tyne: short for Newcastle-upon-Tyne, an English city on the River Tyne in Northumberland, famous for its export of coal.

The Old Ships. James Elroy Flecker's vision of the ancient world was his own. There is an unpublished poem written when he was twenty in which voices call him to "white Aegean isles among the foam" and the dreamy painted lands of the East.

Tyre: an ancient maritime city, capital of Phoenicia, on the eastern shores of the Mediterranean, in modern Lebanon.

Famagusta: seaport on the east coast of Cyprus.

Ææa: (pronounced *Ee eé a*) a small island off the coast of Italy supposed to have been inhabited by Circe—hence its modern name, Monte Circello.

talkative bald-headed seaman: reference to his wooden horse (3 lines below) establishes his identity as Odysseus.

the mast burst open with a rose: this may echo the miracle in the legend of Tannhäuser. When Tannhäuser went on a pilgrimage to Rome to plead forgiveness of his sins before the Pope, he was told it was as impossible for him to be pardoned as for the staff the Pope held in his hand to blossom. Tannhäuser departed for home. Three days later the staff began to put forth green leaves.

Ozymandias. The figure of Ozymandias may be wholly imaginary. However, the tomb of Rameses II at Thebes was called that of Ozymandias by Diodorus Siculus, a Sicilian historian writing in 40 B.C. Rameses II died about 1200 B.C.

Manhole Covers. *Mayan calendar stones*: the Maya Indians, whose civilization flourished in Yucatan, northern Guatemala, and British Honduras (about 200 B.C.–1697 A.D.), had massive stone calendars sculptured in hieroglyphics. They reflect the constant concern of the Mayas with time.

Electrum: a pale yellow alloy of gold and silver used by the ancients in making coins.

artifact: a product of human workmanship, especially of simple workmanship.

Pelicans. *The omnisecular spirit*: a person or an outlook responsive to all ages of the world's history, its past, present, and future. This *spirit* is the antecedent of the pronoun *He,* twice repeated in the closing lines of the poem.

Blue-Butterfly Day. The Spring Azure (blue butterfly) emerges early in spring in the eastern United States, signaling spring's renewal of life.

ridden out desire: mating, laying of eggs.

Chanson Innocent. *goat-footed balloonMan*: identified possibly with the god Pan, usually represented as having the legs and sometimes the ears and horns of a goat.

Group 7

Written on the Eve of Execution. Tichborne was one of six political conspirators in a plot to assassinate Queen Elizabeth and place Mary Queen of Scots on the throne. He was hanged on Sept. 20, 1586, at the age of 28. He wrote the poem in the Tower of London on the night before his execution.

The Victim. *four-o'clocks*: fragrant yellow, red, or white flowers opening late in the afternoon.

Transcendent are the traceries . . . : The poet seems to be suggesting that the colors of the flowers reflected in the window are transcendent, in the sense that they seem more alluring than the flowers themselves.

Reveille. *Forelands beacon*: headlands or promontories lit up with beacon fires in national celebration.

thews that . . . cumber sunlit pallets: muscles, sinews, hence bodily strength that lies lazily in bed once the sun is up.

Crossing the Bar. Tennyson wrote this poem on an October day in his eighty-first year after crossing the Solent, a strait of the English Channel between the mainland and the Isle of Wight, where for forty years he stayed at Farringford within sight and sound of the sea. The "bar" he heard moaning that day at low tide is a shingle bank running out from the mainland for nearly two miles. A few days before his death in 1892 Tennyson requested that "Crossing the Bar" be printed at the end of all editions of his poems.

Turns again home: literally this refers to the turn of the tide, after *flood* or full tide.

Group 8

Deer. *fallow deer*: European deer, so called from their *fallow* or pale yellow color; much smaller than red deer.

phantom . . . Printless as eyelight: in summer the fallow deer are spotted with white; hence, they are camouflaged.

kine: cows.

folded: penned or enclosed, as in a sheepfold.

August: *brazier*: a pan for holding burning coals.

pied: rhymes with pride and means many-colored.

Pastoral. *roots . . . deep in the last century*: Robert Hillyer was born in 1895.

Appendix A

(To be read with **Crystal Moment,** p. 81)

I carried the poem "Crystal Moment" around in me for years. Once, as a boy on a salt-water farm in Maine, I saw a buck deer swim across our bay ahead of three fox hounds. My heart came up into my mouth as the procession of heads passed my skiff, near enough for me to reach it with an oar. I knew instantly that the sight was something tremendous and beautiful and once and for all, though, being only ten years old at the time, I could not put all that into words. But I never forgot it. That procession passed like a light through my mind for years. One time I tried to set it down in so many words in an essay:

An antlered buck, his crested neck set in fine diamonds of rippling water, swimming a bay with hounds yearning in hissing furrows after.

But that was not enough, for the significance of the whole thing was not yet there. That procession reappeared whenever I thought of the things I had seen which were brightest and most alive. It was like a chain that joined years together. For it was a growing thing, and it grew as I grew. It haunted me. I had to put it into words, for it had become a part of me. I tried to write the poem several times. Then late one night I sat down and started to describe the scene, in the order of its details, as simply and as breathlessly as I had seen it. I did not know where the couplets were leading me, or how the poem would end. But I knew for sure that this time it would come to the right ending. I wrote fast, and without changing more than a word here and there. And then, sure enough, as the procession passed from sight, the core of the bright mystery flashed out instantly in the couplet,

Life and death upon one tether
And running beautiful together.

I knew I had reached the end and could rest. I like "Crystal Moment" best of the poems I have written so far, because it seems to me to be a moment made into a monument. . . . It is as if I had taken a single beam of light out of a whole blinding September day and, as the title of my poem suggests, made a crystal out of it. It is a design now, better than life and more lasting, as all poems ought to be.

ROBERT P. TRISTRAM COFFIN

From *Fifty Poets*, edited by William Rose Benét, published by Duffield & Green in 1933.

Appendix B

(To be read with **The Hunchback in the Park,** p. 102)

And the park itself was a world within the world of the seatown [Swansea, in Wales]. . . . Quite near where I lived, so near that on summer evenings I could listen in my bed to the voices of older children playing ball on the sloping paper-littered bank, the park was full of terrors and treasures. Though it was only a little park, it held within its borders of old tall trees, notched with our names and shabby from our climbing, as many secret places, caverns and forests, prairies and deserts, as a country somewhere at the end of the sea.

And though we would explore it one day, armed and desperate, from end to end, from the robbers' den to the pirates' cabin, the highwaymen's inn to the cattle ranch, or the hidden room in the undergrowth, where we held beetle races, and lit the wood fires and roasted potatoes and talked about Africa and the makes of motor cars, yet still the next day, it remained as unexplored as the Poles—a country just born and always changing. . . .

We knew every inhabitant of the park, every regular visitor, every nursemaid, every gardener, every old man. We knew the hour when the alarming retired policeman came in to look at the dahlias and the hour when the old lady arrived in the Bath chair with six Pekinese, and a pale girl to read aloud to her. I think she read the newspaper, but we always said she read the *Wizard*. The face of the old man who sat summer and winter on the bench looking over the reservoir, I can see clearly now, and I wrote a poem long long after I'd left the park and the seatown called "The Hunchback in the Park." . . .

Dylan Thomas

Index of Poems and Poets